3 spooky plays

Bunnicula Presents

JAMES HOWE'S

A BOOK OF

3 spooky plays

Original adaptations by James Howe

Creepy-Crawly Birthday
The Fright Before Christmas
Scared Silly: A Halloween Treat

SCHOLASTIC INC.
New York   Toronto   London   Auckland   Sydney

ISBN 0-590-49759-6

12 11 10 9 8 7 6 5 4 3 2   7 8 9/9 0 1 2/0

Printed in the U.S.A.
First Scholastic printing, October 1997

To my sister-in-law,
Susan Howe —
one terrific teacher!

• CONTENTS •

• INTRODUCTION •

ON A PERSONAL NOTE

When I was a kid, I loved putting on plays with my friends. The one I remember most clearly was called *Dagwood's Awful Day*. It was based on the popular comic strip "Blondie." I wrote the play, directed it, played the part of Dagwood — and sold lemonade during intermission! I don't remember how old I was when I did all that, but by the age of ten I knew I wanted to be an actor when I grew up.

That dream lasted into my twenties. I studied acting in college and even earned a graduate degree in directing after I decided I liked running the show better than being in it. Trying to earn a living in show business, however, was not easy. I finally gave it up and went to work at a regular job.

Then the character of a vampire rabbit hopped into my imagination and led to my first children's book. To my surprise I was a children's author! I love what I do, but sometimes I miss the world of the theater.

In this collection of plays, I've been able to go back to my own childhood, to return to what I myself loved doing years ago — taking favorite characters and bringing them to life on the stage. I'll need some help, though. As the writer, I've provided the dialogue and the action. The rest is up to you.

HOW TO USE THIS BOOK

This *introduction* will give you some basic information about the plays and the characters who appear in all of them. These characters are the members of the Monroe family and their pets: Harold, Chester, and Howie.

The introduction will also give you some tips on putting on a play and define some theatrical terms that will help you in reading the play scripts.

After the introduction, you will find the *scripts* for each of the three plays. At the beginning of each script is a two-sided *program page*. You may reproduce this page, filling in the information on the back, to use as the program for your production.

In the *production notes,* characters who appear only in that particular play will be described. The Monroe family and their pets will only be listed by name because they are described more fully in the introduction. (See "About the Characters" on the next page.) Other production notes will include information about the set, props, costumes and make-up, lighting, and music and sound effects.

ABOUT THE PLAYS

Two of the plays in this collection are about holidays: Halloween and Christmas. However, any of the plays may be performed at any time during the year. One of the ways in which these plays are unique — and fun to put on — is that some of the characters are *animals*.

ABOUT THE CHARACTERS

HAROLD   A large, shaggy dog who is usually dragged into his friend Chester's adventures against his will. Good-natured, reasonable, and a bit on the lazy side.
CHESTER   A cat with a wild imagination. Chester reads a lot, and his reading sometimes goes to his head. He suspects everybody and everything!
HOWIE   A naive wirehaired dachshund puppy who has much to learn. He looks up to Harold and Chester and wants them to like him. Howie has lots of energy; he enjoys cracking jokes.
WHERE'S BUNNICULA?   Although Bunnicula, the vampire rabbit, is a character in the books as well as in these plays, he never speaks and has very little to do. It will be easiest to use a stuffed animal — made to look like Bunnicula, if possible — rather than to have a person play the part.
MR. MONROE   A college professor. Easygoing. A big kid at heart.
MRS. MONROE   A lawyer. More serious than her husband.
PETE MONROE   The older brother, age ten. He sometimes finds his younger brother — and the pets — a nuisance.
TOBY MONROE   The younger brother, age eight. A good kid who loves his pets.

> *Character Note #1:* Consider having girls play any or all of the animals. Also, Toby and/or Pete could be played by girls simply by giving them different names and changing any dialogue that indicates they are boys.
>
> *Character Note #2:* Remember that when the animals speak, they can only be understood by one another. The people never react to them, except as they would to ordinary pets. The animals *do* understand the people, however.
>
> *Character Note #3:* If you are playing one of the animals, you may want to observe real dogs or cats to see how they eat, move, scratch themselves, etc. However, don't try to duplicate their actions exactly. In fact, it will probably be easier for you to be on two feet rather than four.

PUTTING ON A PLAY

The director   The director's job is to see to it that all the parts of the play come together as a whole. In *rehearsal*, or play practice, the director blocks the action. *Blocking the action* means telling the actors where to stand and when and where to move. The director also makes sure that the actors can always be seen and heard. Even though the director has to make many decisions, it is better to think of the director as the *leader*, not the *boss*.

The actors All of the actors make up the *cast* of the play. The actors' basic responsibilities are to come to rehearsals on time, make notes about when and where the director tells them to move, learn their lines, speak clearly and with feeling, and act as naturally as possible. Even when playing animals, you should ask yourself, "How would *I* feel if this were happening to me?"

The stage You don't need a real stage to put on a play. You can put the play on in your classroom, your backyard, or even your living room. The important thing is that the acting area is separate from where the audience sits. You may not be able — or may not want — to set up your stage as I've indicated in the plays in this book. That's fine. You can present your play in any way you want — as long as the audience can see clearly and you have somewhere for your actors to go so they can't be seen when they're offstage.

The set The set refers to the walls, stairs, furniture, etc. that make up the imaginary setting where the play takes place. In the production notes preceding each play you'll find suggestions for the set. However, depending on your own desires or limitations, you can make the set as simple or as detailed as you wish.

Costumes and makeup These plays can be performed without any special costumes or makeup, except in special cases where it is indicated. However, you'll probably have more fun coming up with even simple visual effects to indicate the characters. For the pets, you can use face paints, mop wigs, and animal ears to let the audience know the actor is a dog or a cat. You might give Mr. Monroe some grown-up touches such as glasses and a tie. Mrs. Monroe's hairstyle can give a grown-up impression.

    Costume Note: Other than where it's indicated in *Scared Silly*, don't use face masks. Not only do masks hide the actors' faces but they can make it hard for the audience to understand what the actors are saying.

Props The props, or properties, are the objects that are used in the play. They are either important to the action or are used to decorate the stage. If there are a number of props in the play, it would be a good idea to have one person be in charge of them. The *prop person* makes sure that all the props are set in the right place — either onstage or just offstage where actors can easily get them — before the play begins.

Lighting If you use stage lighting, you will want to dim the lights before the play starts and then bring the lights up on the action. You can darken the lights to a complete *blackout* between scenes and at the end of the play as well.

If you are not using stage lighting, you will need to find other ways to handle beginnings and endings of scenes. If the actors are onstage at the end of a scene, they can simply walk off; then they can walk on again at the beginning of the next scene. Or you can have someone hold a card with large printing that says, for example, SCENE 1: THE MONROES' LIVING ROOM, HALLOWEEN NIGHT, at the beginning of the first scene, and another card that reads, SCENE 2: LATER THAT SAME NIGHT, at the beginning of the second scene.

Music Another helpful way to let the audience know that scenes are beginning or ending is to use music. No music is suggested in the scripts of any of the plays. However, you can use your imagination to create a tape of music that fits the mood of the individual play. Spooky music would fit *Scared Silly*, for instance, while you might use

Christmas carols for *The Fright Before Christmas*. Playing music before a scene begins, then fading it down, will let the audience know the action is about to start. At the end of the scene, you can play music again, and the audience will understand that the scene is over.

Music can also be used under the action to create a mood or add tension to a scene in the same way movies use music. Be careful not to play music when the actors are speaking.

Sound   Some of the plays call for sound effects — wind or rain or an offstage CRASH! You can create these sounds yourself or find tapes of sound effects at a library or music store. If you use taped sound effects — whether copied from another tape or your own creations — you should put *all* the music and sound, in the order in which they occur in the play, on one tape. Then one person should be in charge of running the tape player.

The dress rehearsal   The last rehearsal before the performance is called the dress rehearsal. The actors wear their costumes and makeup. All the props should be in place. The person running the lights and the person running the sound effects and music should practice all their *cues* to be certain they know when to come in.

SOME USEFUL TERMS

Ad-lib	Make up your own words to fit the situation.
Blackout	When the stage lights go out and the stage is dark.
Break a leg!	What people in show business say for "Good luck!"
Cross	Walk, or move; "cross" to the table means "walk" to the table.
Cue	A line of dialogue or action that signals an actor or the person running lights or sound that it is their turn to do something.
Curtain call	When the cast comes onstage at the end of the play to bow as the audience applauds.
Enter	Come onstage.
Exit	Leave the stage.
Improvise	Make up dialogue or action as you go along.
Offstage	Out of sight of the audience.
Onstage	In the playing area in sight of the audience.
Pantomime	Act out without using words or making sounds.
Stage whisper	Not in a full voice, but loud enough for the audience to hear; *implying* that the character is whispering.

IT'S SHOW TIME!

Plan a time and place for your performance. Let people know about it by making flyers or posters and putting them up around your school or neighborhood. Copy the program provided with the plays in this book, or create your own.

Once your performance has begun and you hear the sound of the audience laughing and applauding, you'll know why I loved putting on plays when I was your age. I hope you have the same great feeling about it that I did.

Break a leg!

And don't forget to take a curtain call!

James Howe

• SCARED SILLY: A HALLOWEEN TREAT •
A Play for Halloween
by James Howe

Scene 1: Halloween night. The Monroe family's living room and kitchen.
Scene 2: Later that same night.

CAST
(in order of speaking)

Mr. Monroe, the father _____

Mrs. Monroe, the mother _____

Harold, a dog _____

Chester, a cat _____

Howie, a puppy _____

Toby, the younger brother _____

Pete, the older brother _____

The witch _____

Trick-or-treaters _____

_____

_____

Director _____

Others who helped _____

_____

_____

DATE AND TIME OF PERFORMANCE: _____

PLACE OF PERFORMANCE: _____

• SCARED SILLY: PRODUCTION NOTES •

CHARACTERS

The Monroe family
Mr. Monroe
Mrs. Monroe
Pete
Toby

The pets
Harold, a dog
Chester, a cat
Howie, a puppy

The witch   This character isn't really a witch, but she should look and sound like one. Dress her in a witch's costume and have lots of fun with makeup! The scarier she looks, the better. *Note*: She should *not* wear a mask. Even though the witch's true identity is revealed at the end of the play, she is always referred to in the stage directions as the **witch**. She should speak in a scratchy, "witchy" voice.

Trick-or-treaters   Kids in costumes. Traditional Halloween costumes would be best — ghosts, skeletons, monsters, etc.

THE SET

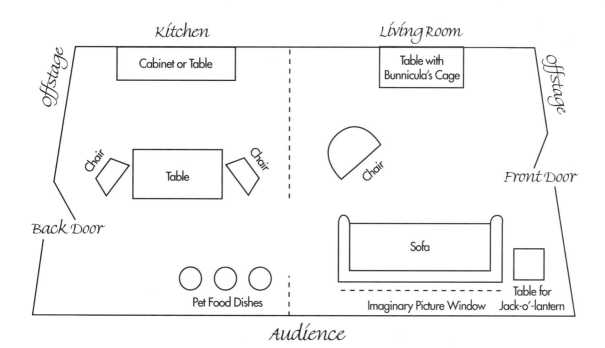

1. There does not need to be a door between the kitchen and living room areas. However, the actors need to pretend that there is a door. There should be an *indication* of a door going from the kitchen to the outdoors and a door going from the living room to the outdoors.

2. The sofa should have its back to the audience so that the audience can see the animals hiding there. The "sofa" can be three chairs in a row.

3. The audience should *imagine* a picture window above and behind the sofa through which the animals watch the parade of trick-or-treaters.

IMPORTANT PROPS

toy rabbit	To "play" the part of Bunnicula.
cage	
jack-o'-lantern	Use a real pumpkin or a plastic one with a flashlight or battery-operated light inside. Don't use a candle.
plastic knife	For Mr. Monroe to *pretend* to carve the pumpkin. The pumpkin should be precut.
needle and thread	For Mrs. Monroe to pretend to sew costumes.
pet food dishes	
dry pet food	Dry cereal will also work as pet food.
suitcase or bag	
one or more flashlights	
a big pot	
ladle or spoon	
bottles of spices	
broom	
doughnuts	
plates	
napkins	
cups or mugs	

COSTUMES AND MAKEUP

The four costumes Mrs. Monroe is "sewing" are later worn by the Monroe family. When she works on them in the first scene, they should not be seen too clearly by the audience. The costumes should be scary enough for the animals to react as if they were seeing "monsters." Be sure the Monroes take off their masks before speaking.

LIGHTING

The second scene is supposed to take place at night during a power failure. If possible, make the stage dim enough to seem dark and spooky but light enough for the audience to see the action. You might consider having a lamp on the set that could be turned on from offstage when the power returns late in the scene. If you can't do anything about lighting, the audience can use their imagination!

MUSIC AND SOUND

There are several indications in the script of "storm" sounds. You can use storm sounds elsewhere in the play, as long as you're careful that the sounds don't make it hard for the actors to be heard.

ABOUT THE HALLOWEEN RAP

You can choose whether or not to include the Halloween Rap between scenes. If you don't include it, simply have a line of kids in costumes or masks cross the stage shouting, "Trick or treat!" If you do include it, you can break it up into individual parts to make memorizing easier. Or the trick-or-treaters can carry the words onstage and read them as they perform.

• SCENE 1 •

*(In the kitchen, **Mr. Monroe** is carving a jack-o'-lantern, while **Mrs. Monroe** sews costumes. **Chester** and **Harold** are at their food dishes, eating. In the living room, **Howie** gazes out the window. **Bunnicula** is in his cage.)*

MR. MONROE:
I love Halloween! It's my favorite holiday.

MRS. MONROE:
That's because you're just a kid at heart, dear.

MR. MONROE:
My mother was the same way. I remember the time —

*(**Harold** makes loud slobbering noises as he eats.)*

MR. MONROE:
Harold!

HAROLD:
(looking up)
Huh?

*(**Mr. Monroe** shakes his head and goes back to work on his jack-o'-lantern.)*

CHESTER:
*(to **Harold**, about his noisy eating)*
Disgusting!

HAROLD:
I can't help it. Halloween makes me hungry.

CHESTER:
Arbor Day makes *you* hungry.

*(**Harold** and **Chester** cross into the living room as they continue to talk.)*

HAROLD:
There's just something about Halloween. Maybe it's all the treats.

CHESTER:
Or all the tricks.

HOWIE:
(nervously)
Tricks? What do you mean?

CHESTER:
(with a sly look)
You'll see.

HOWIE:
What will I see, Uncle Harold?

HAROLD:
Well . . .

CHESTER:
(spooky voice)
It's Halloween. Who knows what may happen?

HOWIE:
I've heard about H-H-Halloween. That's when the goblins come out to play. And the ghosts and the ghouls.

CHESTER:
Don't forget the skeletons. They'd be hurt to the *bone* if you did.

*(Frightened, **Howie** runs to hide behind the sofa.)*

HAROLD:
Nice going, Chester.

*(Enter **Toby** and **Pete**, who race through the living room and into the kitchen.)*

TOBY:
It's not fair! I want to go with you!

PETE:
You walk too slow!

TOBY:

You try to lose me!

MRS. MONROE:

Boys! I have to finish these costumes. I'd like to do it without a headache.

PETE:

But —

MRS. MONROE:

Peter, Toby is going trick-or-treating with you and your friends. And that's that.

PETE:

But —

*(**Mr. Monroe** switches off the lights. A light glows in his finished jack-o'-lantern.*
He holds the jack-o'-lantern in front of him and speaks in a spooky voice.)

MR. MONROE:

I am the spirit of Halloween. Be kind to your brother or else!

PETE:

Oh, Dad . . .

*(**Mr. Monroe** crosses into the living room with the jack-o'-lantern,*
still speaking in a spooky voice.)

MR. MONROE:

I am the spirit of Halloween.

HAROLD, CHESTER, and HOWIE:

(frightened)
Yeow!!

*(**Harold** and **Chester** scamper to join Howie behind the sofa. **Mr. Monroe***
laughs as he places the jack-o'-lantern on the table next to the sofa.)

MR. MONROE:

Someone to watch over you while we're out tonight, boys.

HOWIE:

*(to **Harold** and **Chester**)*
I don't think I like the looks of the baby-sitter.

CHESTER:
(chuckling)
Happy Halloween, kid.

(The four **Monroes** grab their costumes and exit.)

SOUND:
Howling wind and low rumbles of thunder.

• BETWEEN SCENES: A HALLOWEEN RAP •

*(A line of **trick-or-treaters** in costume parades across the stage in front of the living room/kitchen set.)*

TRICK-OR-TREATERS: *(rapping)*

> Yo! We are ghouls,
> We are goblins,
> We're your worse nightmare.
> We play tricks,
> We play games,
> And we don't play fair.
> We are scary,
> We are hairy,
> We are weird beyond compare!
>
> We are trick-or-treating, candy-eating,
> Doorbell-ringing, flashlight-swinging
> Monsters from your neighborhood!
> BOO!
>
> In the daytime
> It's all playtime,
> But at night be watching out!
> 'Cause that creepy-looking creature
> Rings the doorbell of his teacher,
> He's no longer a boy scout!
> And the girl next door with red hair
> Is a zombie with a dead stare
> And she'll really make you shout!
> *(scream)* AAH!
>
> We are trick-or-treating, candy-eating,
> Doorbell-ringing, flashlight-swinging
> Monsters from your neighborhood!
>
> One more time!

We are trick-or-treating, candy-eating,
Doorbell-ringing, flashlight-swinging
Monsters from your neighborhood!
BOO!

(Trick-or-treaters exit.)

• SCENE 2 •

SOUND:
Howling wind and rumbling thunder.

(Harold, Chester, *and* **Howie** *are on the sofa watching out the window as the* **Trick-or-treaters** *exit.* **Howie** *looks scared;* **Harold** *and* **Chester** *do not.)*

HOWIE:
(nervously)
Who were *they*?

CHESTER:
(teasing **Howie***)*
Some goblins looking for puppies to munch.

HAROLD:
(giving **Chester** *a dirty look)*
Kids in costume.

HOWIE:
What's all the noise?

CHESTER:
Creaking bones.

HAROLD:
It's the storm. Chester is trying to scare you, Howie.

HOWIE:
Well, it's working.

HAROLD:
That's the fun of Halloween. There's nothing to be scared of *really*.

SOUND:
Tapping at the front door.

(Harold, Chester, and Howie jump down and hide behind the sofa.)

HOWIE:
Wh-who's at the door?

CHESTER:
Trick-or-treaters. They'll go away.

SOUND:
An even louder tapping at the door.

HAROLD:
Maybe it's the wind.

*(The door creaks opens. A **witch** pokes her head through the doorway, then enters. **Howie** peers around the corner of the sofa and sees the **witch**.)*

HOWIE:
Did you say *witch*?

HAROLD:
I said *wind*.

*(**Harold** and **Chester** look over the top of the sofa and see the **witch**.)*

CHESTER:
(alarmed)
But you meant *witch*!

*(The **animals** remain hidden from the **witch**.
She drops a suitcase-type bag on the floor, looks around, and rubs her hands together.)*

WITCH:
(scratchy voice)
What a night! Is anybody home?

HOWIE:
(a tiny squeak)
No.

WITCH:
What was that?

HOWIE:
(same tiny voice)
Nothing.

WITCH:
Who's there?

HOWIE:
(same voice)
No one.

CHESTER:
(stage whisper)
Ssh! Do you want to end up as a Halloween treat?

*(The **witch** looks around, shrugs, and flips a light switch. Nothing happens.)*

WITCH:
Drat!
(seeing the jack-o'-lantern)
At least there's *some* light.

*(The **witch** picks up the jack-o'-lantern and crosses with it into the kitchen.)*

CHESTER:
*(after the **witch** exits)*
What's a *witch* doing here? I'll tell you what! Bunnicula!

HAROLD and HOWIE:
Bunnicula?

CHESTER:
The vampire rabbit and the witch. They're in cahoots!

HOWIE:
I thought we lived in Centerville.

CHESTER:
Cahoots isn't a place. It means they're cooking something up together.

HAROLD:
I hope it's fudge.

HOWIE:
Or spaghetti. I love spaghetti.

CHESTER:
Maybe it's a witches' brew. Follow me.

*(The **animals** creep toward the kitchen and peek in. The **witch** is stirring something in a big pot. She works by flashlight and the light of the jack-o'-lantern.)*

WITCH:
(adding seasoning to the pot)
A pinch of this and a pinch of that.

CHESTER:
(stage whisper)
Deadly potions.

WITCH:
Bubble, bubble, toil and trouble.

CHESTER:
(stage whisper)
Magic spells.

WITCH:
Now where are those animals?

CHESTER:
(stage whisper)
Big trouble.
(full voice)
Run for it!

*(The **animals** hightail it behind the sofa as
the **witch** enters the living room.)*

WITCH:
Where *are* they? Ah, Bunnicula!

*(The **witch** crosses to **Bunnicula**'s cage, takes the bunny out, and carries him
in her arms to the kitchen. She puts him on the table and opens a bottle of spices
which she sprinkles into the pot.)*

CHESTER:
*(after the **witch** exits)*
My mother didn't raise me to be an ingredient. Let's get out of here!

HOWIE:
But . . . but we've got to save Bunnicula.

CHESTER:
Aw, that's sweet.

HAROLD:
Chester, you *do* have a heart.

CHESTER:
Of course I do. Let's march right in there and say, "Excuse us, Ms. Witch. Why don't you take one of us instead? You don't want to ruin your witches' brew with a *rabbit*, do you?"

HOWIE:
Yuck. There's nothing worse than a hare in your soup.

HAROLD:
Wait a minute, Chester.

CHESTER:
Listen, you two, the only way out is through the kitchen.
We'll have to move fast to get past her.

HAROLD:
*(to **Howie**)*
Don't worry. I'll save Bunnicula.

*(The **animals** burst into the kitchen, crashing into their dishes and scattering food all over. The startled **witch** tosses the contents of the spice jar she's holding into the air.)*

WITCH:
Oh, my stars!

CHESTER:
*(to **Harold** and **Howie**)*
Hurry!

*(**Harold** grabs **Bunnicula** with his teeth and joins **Chester** and **Howie***

*in their race for the back door. The door opens and **Toby** and **Pete**,
completely disguised by their scary costumes, enter.)*

CHESTER:
(screaming)
Monsters!
*(The **animals** turn around and race through the living room toward the front door.
Toby, **Pete**, and the **witch** follow. As the **animals** reach the door, it flies open.
Mr. and **Mrs. Monroe**, also disguised by their costumes, enter. **Harold** drops
Bunnicula. **Toby** picks him up.)*

CHESTER:
(hysterical)
Monsters everywhere! We're doomed! Trapped by a horrible —

*(The lights pop on. **Mr. Monroe** takes off his mask.)*

MR. MONROE:
Mom! What are you doing here?

CHESTER:
Mom? We're trapped by a horrible . . . *(pause)* . . . Mom?

*(**Toby** removes his mask.)*

TOBY:
(happily surprised)
Grandma!

*(**Mrs. Monroe** and **Pete** remove their masks.)*

PETE:
(also happily surprised)
You weren't supposed to come until tomorrow.

WITCH:
I thought I'd arrive early and surprise you. You know Halloween is my favorite holiday!

MRS. MONROE:
Like mother, like son.

MR. MONROE:
Your costume is great. But what's wrong with your voice?

WITCH:

Oh, I have an awful cold. To think I traveled here in this storm! And then, just as I got to the house, the power went out. I brought Bunnicula into the kitchen to keep me company while I made hot cider. But the *strangest* thing happened. All of a sudden, the other three charged into the room and —

TOBY:

Cider? Let's have some!

MR. MONROE:

I made doughnuts this morning.

HAROLD:

(dreamily)
Doughnuts.

WITCH:

Doughnuts and cider. Oh, I *love* Halloween.

MR. MONROE:

That's because you're just a kid at heart, Mom.

*(The four **Monroes** and the **witch** cross into the kitchen.
The **witch** takes a broom and sweeps up the spilled spices and pet food.
The rest of the **Monroes** get out dishes, napkins, doughnuts, etc.
In the living room, **Harold** and **Howie** glare at **Chester**.)*

CHESTER:

What? She *could* be a witch, you know.

*(**Harold** and **Howie** shake their heads, fed up with **Chester**.
They cross into the kitchen as **Chester** follows.)*

CHESTER:

(as they cross)
Okay, okay, she looks a little like Mr. Monroe's mother under that costume and makeup. And she sounds a little like Mr. Monroe's mother under that scratchy voice. But she could be a witch *pretending* to be Mr. Monroe's mother. Couldn't she?

HAROLD:

Nonsense.

HOWIE:
Stop trying to scare us.

MR. MONROE:
*(as the **animals** enter)*
By the way, Mom, how was your flight?

WITCH:
(holding the broom)
Bumpy. But I still say flying is the only way to travel.

HOWIE:
(his jaw dropping as he stares at the broom)
Flying?!

CHESTER:
(his eyes growing wide)
I was right!

*(As the **family** watches, **Howie** and **Chester** race out of the kitchen and run to hide behind the sofa. **Harold** looks back and forth between the doughnuts and his friends, then runs to join them.)*

HAROLD:
Move over, you two. It's going to be a long night!

*(The **family** sneaks into the living room, peers over the top of the sofa.)*

FAMILY:
BOO!

HAROLD, CHESTER, and HOWIE:
YEOW!

*(The **family** laughs as the **animals** cower behind the sofa, paws over their eyes.)*

HAROLD:
(to the audience)
Wake me up when it's Thanksgiving!

*(The **trick-or-treaters** enter, performing the Halloween Rap. The **entire cast** joins in.)*

• THE FRIGHT BEFORE CHRISTMAS •
A Play for Christmas
by James Howe

Scene 1: Late Christmas Eve. The Monroe family's living room.
Scene 2: Later that night. The storage room.
Scene 3: Minutes later. The living room.

CAST
(in order of speaking)

Mr. Monroe, the father   _____

Pete, the older brother   _____

Mrs. Monroe, the mother   _____

Toby, the younger brother   _____

Harold, a dog   _____

Chester, a cat   _____

Howie, a puppy   _____

Director   _____

Others who helped   _____

                                _____

                                _____

DATE AND TIME OF PERFORMANCE: _____

PLACE OF PERFORMANCE: _____

• THE FRIGHT BEFORE CHRISTMAS: PRODUCTION NOTES •

CHARACTERS

The Monroe family
Mr. Monroe
Mrs. Monroe
Pete
Toby

The pets
Harold, a dog
Chester, a cat
Howie, a puppy

THE SET

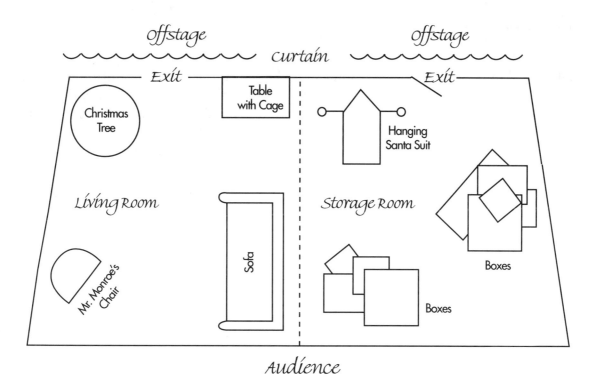

1. The stage doesn't have to be set up exactly as pictured. However, the two playing areas should be separated in some way, implying that they are not right next to each other. The actors should not exit from one playing area directly into the other.

2. Ideally, the "storage area" part of the set should be dark or hidden while the action takes place in the "living room," and vice versa. If you can't accomplish this with lights, try hanging a curtain to hide one side of the stage while the other is in use.

IMPORTANT PROPS

toy rabbit	To "play" the part of Bunnicula, although he is never really seen in this play. Still, his cage should be onstage.
cage	
Christmas tree	Doesn't have to be real; you can make one out of cardboard or paint it on a large sheet of paper.
presents	To appear under the tree in the third scene. These should *not* be under the tree in the first scene. If the living room is hidden during the second scene, the presents can easily be placed out of the audience's view. If the audience is going to see the presents being placed under the tree, it might be fun to have them put there by someone dressed as Santa Claus!
large book	
chew-bone	
boxes and junk	You can make the storage room as cluttered as you want. The more for the pets to crash into, the better! However, be sure you don't use anything that will be damaged or hurt the actors when they crash into it. Empty boxes with lots of empty cans inside are lightweight and make plenty of noise!
clothesline or hook	For hanging the Santa Claus costume (see below).

COSTUMES AND MAKEUP

In the first scene, the Monroe family can either be dressed in regular clothes or pajamas and bathrobes. They should definitely be dressed in nightwear for the third scene. Pete needs to be wearing socks in the first scene.

SPECIAL COSTUME/PROP NOTE

The Santa Claus costume functions both as a prop and a costume. As a *prop*, be sure that it is hung in a way that makes it difficult for the audience to see clearly what it is. Lighting can help this — or you might hang it so that it is partially hidden from view. As a *costume*, a beard and Santa hat, with the coat thrown loosely over Harold's shoulders, will create the best effect — and be the easiest to get on in a hurry. Don't try to get the actor into pants (it will take too long). And don't use a mask!

LIGHTING

If possible, use lighting to create shadowy, spooky effects during the second scene. A lamp during the first and third scenes will suggest nighttime.

MUSIC AND SOUND

You can create offstage crashes by dropping a box (out of sight of the audience, of course) that is loosely filled with empty tin cans.

If you want to play music to introduce scenes and breaks, Christmas carols would work well — as would spooky music, since the play is also about "ghosts."

At the end of the play, you might choose to have the cast lead the audience in some Christmas carols. Upbeat, lively carols are best. Some possibilities are "Deck the Halls," "Jingle Bells," and "Santa Claus Is Comin' to Town." You might want to pass out song sheets so the audience can sing along.

• SCENE 1: The Living Room •

*(**Mr. Monroe** is sitting in a chair, reading aloud from a large book. **Mrs. Monroe** sits nearby, listening. Toby and Pete lie on the floor, listening. **Pete** is on his back, one leg crossed over the other, a sock dangling from his foot. **Harold, Chester,** and **Howie** are also listening. **Howie** chews on a bone, but is distracted by **Pete's** dangling sock during **Mr. Monroe's** speech. We don't necessarily see **Bunnicula**, but his cage is in the room.)*

MR. MONROE:
(reading in a dramatic voice)
"The bell struck twelve. Scrooge looked about him for the Ghost, and saw it not.
As the last stroke ceased to vibrate, he remembered the prediction of old Jacob Marley,
and lifting up his eyes, beheld a solemn phantom, draped and hooded, coming, like a
mist along the ground, towards him."

*(**Howie** lunges for **Pete's** sock, grabs it with his teeth, and runs off.
Pete jumps up and chases him.)*

PETE:
Howie, give me that sock!

*(**Pete** and **Howie** get into a tug-of-war with the sock.)*

PETE:
Bad dog! How many times do I have to tell you —

MRS. MONROE:
Peter, for heaven's sake! He's only a puppy.

TOBY:
Yeah, and it's only a sock.
*(under his breath, to **Harold**)*
And a smelly one, too!

HAROLD:
*(to **Chester**)*
Yuck!

PETE:
(to Toby)
That's not the point.

MR. MONROE:
(closing the book)
You're right. The point is that it's time for bed.

TOBY:
Aw, Dad. Aren't you going to finish reading *A Christmas Carol?*

MR. MONROE:
Tomorrow.

TOBY:
But you were just getting to the best part.
(spooky voice)
The Ghost of Christmas Yet to Come!

MRS. MONROE:
It's late, boys. We'd better get to sleep or Santa won't have time to visit us.

*(**Howie** suddenly lets go of the sock, which sends **Pete** tumbling backward onto the floor. **Howie** runs and hides behind a piece of furniture. Everyone laughs at **Pete**.)*

PETE:
What got into *him* all of a sudden?
(looking at his sock with disgust)
This sock is covered with dog spit.

TOBY:
That's an improvement.

MR. MONROE:
Toby. Pete. It's Christmas Eve, remember? Good behavior.

PETE:
Yeah, yeah. Somebody tell that to Howie, okay?

MRS. MONROE:
(standing up)
All right, Peter, I'll be sure to have a long talk with Howie about it in the morning. Right now, it's bedtime.

*(The **Monroes** exit. As they go:)*

TOBY:
That Charles Dickens is a good writer, isn't he, Dad?

MR. MONROE:
One of the best, Toby, one of the best.

*(After the family exits, **Chester** jumps up on the chair and opens the book.)*

HAROLD:
Chester, what are you doing?

CHESTER:
I've got to find out how it ends.

*(As **Chester** starts to read, **Howie** pokes his head out from where he's hidden.)*

HOWIE:
Psst! Uncle Harold!

HAROLD:
Yes, Howie?

HOWIE:
I'm scared.

HAROLD:
What are you scared of? It's Christmas. Just think, soon we'll go to sleep and Santa will come with his big bag over his shoulder and —

HOWIE:
(whimpering)
I don't want Santa to come.

HAROLD:
But —

CHESTER:
Hey, listen to this.
(reading in a spooky voice)
"There were ghostly eyes intently fixed upon him, while he — "

HOWIE:
(frightened)
Yeow!

*(**Howie** scampers from the room, as **Harold** and **Chester** watch him go.)*

CHESTER:
Boy, talk about your high-strung pup!

HAROLD:
I think he's scared of Santa Claus.

CHESTER:
Don't be ridiculous, Harold. It's obvious what's frightening him.

HAROLD:
Huh?

CHESTER:
Ghosts.

HAROLD:
Ghosts? It's Christmas Eve, Chester, not Halloween.

CHESTER:
Think of Scrooge's Christmas Eve, Harold.
(reading in a spooky voice)
"The air was filled with phantoms, wandering hither and thither in restless haste,
and moaning as they went."
*(**Chester** yawns, curls up, and closes his eyes, then opens them again.)*
Good night, Harold. Sweet dreams.
*(**Chester** closes his eyes again and starts to snore.)*

HAROLD:
(who hasn't moved)
Sweet dreams, huh? Thanks, Chester. Thanks a lot.
*(**Harold** curls up to go to sleep. He closes his eyes. Suddenly they pop open.)*
What was that?
(to audience)
Did you hear anything? A ghost, maybe? A phantom wandering hither and thither in
restless haste? No? I guess it was just my imagination.

*(**Harold** closes his eyes again. In a minute, he and **Chester** are both snoring up a storm.)*

SOUND:
An offstage crash!

(Harold and **Chester** jerk awake.)

CHESTER:
What was that?

HAROLD:
Just my imagination.

SOUND:
Another loud crash!

CHESTER:
You have a very real imagination, Harold.

HAROLD:
Noisy, too.

CHESTER:
You know what I think?

HAROLD:
I'm afraid to ask.

CHESTER:
Ghosts.

HAROLD:
Ghosts?

CHESTER:
Ghosts. We'd better check the house.

(Harold and **Chester** move through the audience, searching and ad-libbing as they go:)

HAROLD and CHESTER:
Here, ghost, ghost. See any ghosts? No ghosts here. Nope, no ghosts. Did you find any?
No, did you? I don't see any ghosts. Did anybody see any ghosts?

(They end up back onstage.)

HAROLD:
No ghosts, Chester.

CHESTER:
Then what made that noise?
*(Eyeing **Bunnicula's** cage.)*
Ah-ha!

HAROLD:
Ah-ha-*who*?

CHESTER:
It's Bunnicula, of course.

HAROLD:
Chester, Bunnicula is a rabbit, not a ghost.

CHESTER:
He's a *vampire* rabbit. Who knows what weird stuff he's up to?

*(They cross to **Bunnicula's** cage and peer in.)*

HAROLD:
*(putting **Chester** on)*
He's twitching his whiskers, Chester. That's weird. Oh, oh. Now he's licking his front paw and washing his ear. Very weird. Look out! He's . . . he's hopping. Run for cover!

CHESTER:
*(giving **Harold** a long look)*
Through amusing yourself, Harold?

HAROLD:
I think so.

CHESTER:
Good, then let's keep looking for . . .

***SOUND*:**
A loud offstage crash!

HAROLD and CHESTER:
Ghosts!!

BLACKOUT.

• SCENE 2: The Storage Room •

*(The storage room is full of boxes and clutter. **Howie** is hidden from view behind a big pile of boxes. Half-hidden in shadow is a hanging Santa Claus costume. It should look spooky enough to startle **Harold** and **Chester**, and what it is should not be obvious to the audience. **Harold** and **Chester** enter, looking about cautiously. At first, they speak in stage whispers.)*

HAROLD:

Are you sure that crash came from in here, Chester?

CHESTER:

We've looked everywhere else. The Monroes are sound asleep in their beds. Howie is curled up under the kitchen table. It had to have come from in here.

HAROLD:

But I don't like it here. It's dark and full of . . .
*(**Harold** gasps when he sees the hanging Santa Claus costume.)*

CHESTER:

What is it, Harold?

HAROLD:

There, straight ahead. Don't you see it?

CHESTER:

(seeing it)
The ghost! Stand back. I'll take care of this.

*(**Chester** goes into a cat crouch, head down, rear end wiggling in the air. He prepares himself to attack. He prepares a little too long.)*

HAROLD:

*(fed up with how long **Chester** is taking)*
Attack, already!

*(**Chester** wiggles his rear end one last time, takes a running leap, and attacks the costume, which falls on top of him.)*

HAROLD:

Hey, that isn't a ghost. It's Mr. Monroe's Santa Claus costume.
*(**Chester** pokes his head out from under it.)*
Red becomes you, Chester. You should wear it more often. Say, I have an idea.

CHESTER:

(sarcastically)
Does it involve accessories?

HAROLD:

(ignoring him)
I'll put the suit on and pretend to be Santa. When Howie wakes up, he'll see a *friendly* Santa Claus — his old pal Harold — and he won't be afraid.

CHESTER:

If Santa Claus is what he's afraid of.

HAROLD:

Come on, Chester, lend me a paw.

*(**Chester** helps **Harold** into the suit. Suddenly, the big pile of boxes moves. **Chester** and **Harold** cross slowly toward it, **Harold** behind **Chester**.)*

CHESTER:

Okay, ghost, come out and show yourself!

HAROLD:

*(stage whisper to **Chester**)*
Aren't ghosts invisible?

CHESTER:

Don't bother me with details, Harold.
(to the pile of boxes)
You hear me, ghost? We know you're in there. The game is up. The show is over.
You've haunted your last house, rattled your last chain, booed your last boo.
It's time to throw in the sheet, it's —

HAROLD:

(to audience)
If the ghost wasn't dead already, this would *kill* him.

*(The pile moves again and out comes . . . **Howie!** **Harold** is positioned in such a way that **Howie** doesn't see him clearly at first.)*

HOWIE:

Okay, okay, I get the picture.

CHESTER:

Howie! What are you doing there?

HOWIE:

I was trying to hide from Santa Claus. I bunched up my rug under the kitchen table so he'd think I was asleep and wouldn't come looking for me.

HAROLD:

*(chuckling, as he moves closer to **Howie**)*
So you're our Christmas ghost.

*(**Howie** sees **Harold** and gasps.)*

HOWIE:

Santa!!

*(**Howie** dashes for the door, barking and knocking over boxes and junk as he goes. **Harold** and **Chester** chase after him, barking and meowing and making a lot of noise. All three collide as the door flies open and **Mrs. Monroe**, **Toby**, and **Pete** appear.)*

MRS. MONROE:

What is going on down here?

TOBY:

Harold! How come you're dressed up like Santa Claus?

PETE:

Look, Mom, it's a total mess in here. I'll bet it's all Howie's fault.
He's been bad all week.
*(**Pete** goes to **Howie** and wags his finger at him.)*
This time the dogcatcher really will come and get you.

TOBY:

The dogcatcher? What are you talking about?

PETE:

On Monday, Howie ate the last page of my mystery book. On Thursday, he broke my plastic skeleton that took me two whole weeks to put together. I told him if he didn't stop wrecking my stuff, the dogcatcher would come with his bag and take him away.

*(**Howie** whimpers loudly. **Mrs. Monroe** goes to him and pets him.)*

MRS. MONROE:
Poor Howie. No dogcatcher is going to take you away. You can't help it if you break things sometimes. You're just a puppy. You still have a lot to learn.

MR. MONROE:
(appearing in the doorway)
So this is where all the noise is coming from. What do you suppose they're so excited about?

TOBY:
Christmas, I'll bet. Nobody can sleep the night before Christmas.

MR. MONROE:
Well, I know somebody else who hasn't been sleeping.

PETE and TOBY:
Santa Claus!

*(**Pete** and **Toby** exit excitedly.*
***Mr.** and **Mrs. Monroe** laugh and start to exit, too. They look back at the **animals**.)*

MRS. MONROE:
Well, come on. Santa brought some goodies for you, too.

*(**Mr.** and **Mrs. Monroe** exit.)*

HAROLD:
*(to **Chester**)*
Shall we? Or do you want to stay down here with the ghosts?

CHESTER:
Bah, humbug.
(as they leave)
Just one thing, you guys.

HOWIE:
What?

HAROLD:
What now, Chester?

CHESTER:
I get to play with the ribbons.

HAROLD:
Whatever you say, Chester. Whatever you say.

(They exit.)

BLACKOUT.

• SCENE 3: The Living Room •

*(The setting is the same as Scene 1, except that there are now many wrapped presents under the tree. The **Monroes** are gathered around the tree. As the **animals** enter, **Howie** stops and stares, wide-eyed.)*

HOWIE:
Did Santa Claus bring all this stuff?

HAROLD:
Of course. That's what I was trying to tell you. He carries presents in his bag and leaves them under Christmas trees all over the world.

HOWIE:
And *I* thought he used that bag to carry off bad puppies. That's what Pete said. At least that's what I *thought* he said. Maybe he was talking about the dogcatcher, and I thought he meant Santa Claus. Mrs. Monroe is right, Uncle Harold. I do have a lot to learn.

HAROLD:
Don't worry, we'll teach you everything you need to know. Won't we, Chester?

CHESTER:
(muttering to himself)
I still say there were ghosts.

HAROLD:
*(to **Howie**)*
Then again, maybe we'd better leave the teaching to me.

*(**Toby** runs to the **animals** and gives each of them a present.)*

TOBY:
Merry Christmas, you guys.

MR. MONROE:
(picking up the book)
Shall we read a little more and then open our presents?
*(reading as the **family** and **pets** gather round him)*

"The phantom slowly, gravely, silently approached."

CHESTER:
(shuddering, to audience)
And to all a Good Fright!

BLACKOUT.

*(The lights come back up. The **entire cast** leads the audience in singing some lively Christmas carols. See **Music and Sound** production notes on page 27.)*

• CREEPY-CRAWLY BIRTHDAY •

by James Howe

Place: The Monroe family's living room and den.
Time: Toby's birthday.

CAST
(in order of speaking)

Mr. Monroe, the father   _____

Pete, the older brother   _____

Harold, a dog   _____

Mrs. Monroe, the mother   _____

Toby, the younger brother   _____

Howie, a puppy   _____

Chester, a cat   _____

Party animals   Party guests

_____   _____

_____   _____

_____   _____

_____   _____

Director   _____

Others who helped   _____

                                          _____

                                          _____

DATE AND TIME OF PERFORMANCE: _____

PLACE OF PERFORMANCE: _____

• CREEPY-CRAWLY BIRTHDAY: PRODUCTION NOTES •

CHARACTERS

The Monroe family
Mr. Monroe
Mrs. Monroe
Pete
Toby

The pets
Harold, a dog
Chester, a cat
Howie, a puppy

Mr. Hu The owner of "Hu's Zoo."

The party animals   The seven animals suggested in the play are based on the book version of **Creepy-Crawly Birthday**. In fact, a different number and different kinds of animals may be used, although the boa constrictor — the only animal that actually speaks — should be included. The animals are played by actors, using face paints and/or costume elements to suggest what they are.

The party animals are always referred to as "animals" in the play script. Harold, Chester, and Howie are referred to as the "pets."

The party guests   The guests are Toby's friends, so they should appear to be his age. Include boys and girls. Six to eight is probably the best number.

THE SET

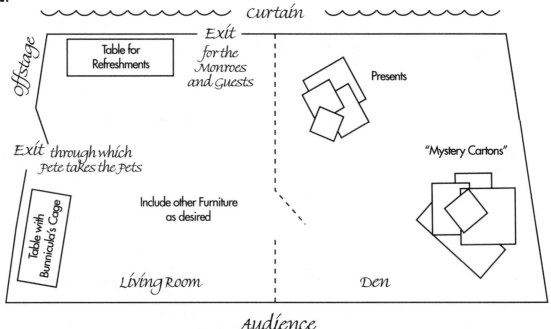

1. There does not need to be a door between the living room and den, or the living room and the offstage room where Pete takes the pets. However, the actors need to pretend that there is a door. When Pete takes the pets away, they must actually leave the stage and not be seen. In the den they remain in view, except when they hide.

2. When the doorbell rings and Toby exits to answer it, he should use a *different* exit from the one Pete uses with the pets. The diagram opposite indicates one way to handle this.

IMPORTANT PROPS

toy rabbit	To "play" the part of Bunnicula, although he is never really seen in this play. Still, his cage should be onstage.
cage	
refreshments	Need not be real food; include paper plates, cups, etc.
decorations	Balloons, streamers, a banner, etc.
birthday cake	Since this is going to end up on Mr. Monroe, it is probably best not to waste a real cake. You can make a cake out of a big piece of foam, cut in whatever shape you want and covered with shaving cream. Put candles on it (but don't light them!), and it will look like the real thing.
presents	Wrap some empty boxes and put them in the den as if they were gifts from Toby's family. Also give each guest a wrapped box to carry.
cartons	The large "mystery cartons" (opposite) need to be big enough to hold the actors who play the animals. Punch holes in them and paint latches on them to give the impression that they contain animals. Cut doors in them for the actor/animals to escape through. While *seven* cartons are indicated in the script, use whatever number suits your production.
sign	Should have writing large enough for the audience to read: HU'S ZOO: UNUSUAL ANIMALS FOR YOUR PARTY.

COSTUMES AND MAKEUP

Since part of the party supposedly takes place in the backyard, dress your actors in "warm weather" clothes. Party clothes are fun but not necessary.

As for the party animals, be creative with face paints and/or costume elements to suggest the kinds of animals. Don't feel you have to costume each animal realistically.

MUSIC AND SOUND

A real doorbell, found in any hardware store, can be used. If you have trouble finding a bell, simply have the actors knock — LOUDLY — offstage.

The familiar refrain of "Happy birthday to you" that is sung at most birthday parties is actually a copyrighted song. If it is performed in a production where admission is charged, a fee for its use must be paid. You need not worry about this for backyard or classroom productions. However, you might wish to use a different birthday song or write one of your own!

(Two rooms are visible to the audience: the living room and the den. The den contains wrapped presents and the seven "mystery cartons" (on diagram p.42). In the living room, **Harold, Chester,** *and* **Howie** *are sleeping.* **Bunnicula's** *cage is on a table. After a moment,* **Mr. Monroe, Mrs. Monroe, Toby,** *and* **Pete,** *carrying refreshments and decorations, burst into the room, startling the pets awake. While the* **Monroes** *set up for a party, the* **pets** *try to get their attention. The dialogue begins as the* **Monroes** *enter and should be said quickly, with some overlapping.)*

MR. MONROE:

(crossing to the table)
Peter, help me out with these refreshments, will you?

PETE:
Okay, Dad.

HAROLD:

(rising, crossing to the table)
Did I hear "refreshments"?

MRS. MONROE:
Can someone take the other end of this banner?

TOBY:
I will.

MR. MONROE:
I hope we can get all this food taken care of before the guests arrive.

HOWIE:

(crossing to the table)
Did I hear "food"?

*(***Howie** *joins* **Harold.** *Both whimper and beg, ignored by* **Mr. Monroe** *and* **Pete.** **Chester** *watches this canine display with disgust.)*

TOBY:
Pete, what did you do with the party bags?

PETE:
I don't know.

TOBY:
You had them just a minute ago.

PETE:

They're in the kitchen, I think. Or maybe upstairs. Or on the back porch.

TOBY:

If you lost them . . .

PETE:

Relax, would you? We'll find them.

HAROLD:

(to **Mr. Monroe,** *eyeing the food he is putting out*)
Uh, excuse me, remember us?

HOWIE:

We're your dogs. We haven't eaten in, gee, at least —

HAROLD:

Twenty minutes.

(**Harold** *and* **Howie** *woof and whimper.* **Chester** *rolls his eyes.*)

CHESTER:

You two are pathetic. Are there no depths to which you wouldn't sink?

HOWIE:

You mean when it comes to food?

(**Chester** *nods.* **Harold** *and* **Howie** *look at each other, then back at* **Chester.***)*

HAROLD and HOWIE:

No, I don't think so, no.

MR. MONROE:

Oh, hello there, boys, what do you want?

HAROLD:

(surprised, to **Howie**)
I thought we were pretty obvious, didn't you?

(**Howie** *nods, as* **Chester** *jumps down and crosses to them.*)

CHESTER:

Dogs never do anything right. Rule number one: Always hit up the softest touch.

*(**Chester** saunters over to **Toby** and tries to get his attention by doing catlike things:*
rolling around on the floor, rubbing up against him, etc. He speaks at the same time:)
Hi, it's me, your cat. Remember how much you love me? How about a little token of your
affection? Something edible maybe. I see some chips over on that table, a little dip,
how about those fish-shaped crackers? I don't suppose you'd have any tuna, would ya?
How about —

TOBY:
(finally noticing him)
Oh, hi, Chester.

PETE:
Don't you mean, "Good-bye, Chester?"

TOBY:
Very funny.

PETE:
Well, you know he's got to go. They all do.

*(**Chester** shoots a worried look at **Harold** and **Howie**, who shrug.*
*They don't know what **Pete** is talking about.)*

TOBY:
It's *my* birthday. If I want them to stay —

MR. MONROE:
You can't have everything, son. You told us you wanted —

TOBY:
I know, I know.

MRS. MONROE:
Pete, why don't you take them now?

PETE:
Okay.
*(He picks up **Bunnicula**'s cage and crosses to a door on one side of the stage.)*
Come on, you guys, let's go.

MR. MONROE:
(alarmed)
Not *that* room, Pete.

PETE:
Oh, right, sorry.
(He crosses to a door on the other side of the stage and calls out.)
Harold, Howie, Chester! Come on, you guys, let's go!

*(Reluctantly, the **pets** follow **Pete** through the second door.)*

PETE:
(returning without them or the cage)
Phew! It's a good thing I didn't put them in the den.

TOBY:
I'll say.

MR. MONROE:
(looking at his watch)
Look at the time. We'd better get the backyard set up before your friends get here, Toby.

TOBY:
Okay.
*(to **Pete**)*
And you'd better find those party bags.

PETE:
Yeah, yeah.

*(The **Monroes** exit. After a moment, **Chester** pokes his head into the room.)*

CHESTER:
The coast is clear.

*(**Harold** and **Howie** follow **Chester** into the room. They all stare at the door to the den.)*

CHESTER:
Are you thinking what I'm thinking?

HOWIE:
I don't know. Are you thinking, "When do we eat?"

CHESTER:
I'm thinking that there's something they don't want us to know about.
And it's behind *that* door.

HAROLD:

I saw them putting Toby's presents in there earlier.
You don't suppose it's one of his presents, do you?

CHESTER:

I don't know. But we're about to find out.

HAROLD:

Oh, good. Let me know what you discover.

CHESTER:

I said *we*, Harold.

HOWIE:

*(admiringly, to **Chester**)*
Gee, I didn't know you spoke French.

CHESTER:

*(ignoring **Howie**)*
Follow me.

*(The **pets** creep up to the door, sniffing at it when they reach it.)*

HOWIE:

Something smells funny.

*(They push open the door and enter, immediately spotting the seven large cartons
among the wrapped presents.)*

HAROLD:

What are those?

HOWIE:

(wrinkling his nose as he sniffs the cartons)
Whatever's inside, I think its sale date has expired.

(One of the cartons moves.)

CHESTER:

Watch out, men! It's alive!

*(**Harold** and **Howie** back away as another carton moves.)*

HAROLD:
What do you think's in there, Chester?

CHESTER:
(nodding his head wisely)
I *know* what's in there, Harold. And now it all makes sense.

HOWIE:
It doesn't just make sense; it *stinks*!

HAROLD:
So what's inside? Tell us, Chester.

CHESTER:
Isn't it obvious? It's —

SOUND:
Doorbell.

CHESTER:
Quiet! We don't want them to know we're in here.

*(The **pets** hide as **Toby** enters the living room with two **guests**. The brief party scene that follows should be improvised and the dialogue ad-libbed. **Mr.** and **Mrs. Monroe** and **Pete** enter the living room. The **doorbell** rings on and off; Toby runs to get it and returns with more **guests**, one or two at a time. Each guest gives **Toby** a present. **Toby** or another member of the **Monroe family** takes each present and puts it with the others in the room where the **pets** are hiding. The **family** and **guests** might play a game or just ad-lib dialogue until all the **guests** have arrived and the last of the presents has been taken into the room with the **pets**. This action should move along quickly.)*

MR. MONROE:
*(above the noise, to **Toby**)*
Toby, why don't we take your guests out back where the games are set up?

TOBY:
Okay, Dad. Everybody, follow me!

*(**Toby** leads everyone offstage. After a moment's silence, the **pets** come out from hiding, but remain in the den.)*

HAROLD:
So, Chester, you were saying?

CHESTER:
I was saying that there are *animals* in those boxes!

HOWIE:
Animals?

HAROLD:
Why would they give Toby animals for a present?
(pause)
Unless . . .

CHESTER:
Exactly.

HOWIE:
(not getting it)
Unless exactly what?

CHESTER:
(dramatically)
Unless they're replacing us!
(Howie *gasps.)*
Pete said we had to *go*, right? The way I figure it, Toby told his parents he wanted new
pets for his birthday. And Mr. and Mrs. Monroe — the traitors — said okay,
but the old pets would have to go!

HOWIE:
(sniffing tearfully)
But *I'm* not old. I'm still a puppy.

CHESTER:
Well, I'm not going to stand for it.

HAROLD:
Me, either.

HOWIE:
Me, either.
(Howie *sits.)*

HAROLD:
Now what?

CHESTER:
Don't worry. I have a plan.
(pause)
We're going to let them loose.

HAROLD:
(shocked)
We're what?!

CHESTER:
We're going to let them loose. Listen, they're strange animals in a strange place.
They'll start running around, acting crazy. All we have to do is sit quietly on the side-
lines: the well-behaved, perfect pets.

HAROLD:
Hmm, it just might work.

CHESTER:
It *has* to work — or it's the pound for us.

*(**Harold** and **Howie** look at each other, aghast, then back at **Chester**.)*

HAROLD:
Let's get going.

*(The **pets** sniff around the cartons, trying to figure out how to open them.)*

HOWIE:
I don't suppose anybody has a Swiss army knife.

HAROLD:
Here's a latch. I think I can lift it with my nose.

CHESTER:
There's a latch here, too.

*(Using their paws and noses, the three **pets** lift the latches of the seven cartons.
They then stand back and wait. Nothing moves. Finally one carton, then another, then
another . . . shake and quake and rattle and rock. The **pets**' eyes widen in anticipation of
what is going to come out of those boxes. This anticipation should be shared by the
audience. Build to . . . seven **animals:** a **lizard**, a **snake**, a **hedgehog**, a **dove**, a **frog**, a
rat, and a **bat**, who slither, crawl, leap, and fly out of the boxes, making
appropriate animal noises.)*

CHESTER:

Leapin' lizards!

HOWIE:

These are the weirdest-looking dogs and cats I ever saw!

HAROLD:

Let's get out of here!

*(They run through the door into the living room, followed by the **animals**. At the same time, **Mr. Monroe**, carrying a birthday cake, comes into the living room, from the opposite direction, leading **Toby**, **Pete**, **Mrs. Monroe**, and the **guests**. Pandemonium! The **animals** and **pets** go crazy, one of them crashing into **Mr. Monroe**, sending the cake flying. The **guests** panic, screaming and running in all directions. The following dialogue takes place during the action.)*

GUEST #1:

Snakes!

GUEST #2:

Rats!

GUEST #3:

Creepy-crawlies everywhere!

TOBY:

Mom, look at my cake!

PETE:

How did *they* get in here?!

GUEST #4:

What kind of party *is* this?

GUEST #5:

*(to **Toby**)*
Wait'll my mom hears about this, Toby Monroe!
She'll never let me come to *your* house again!

GUEST #6:

I thought there was going to be a clown!

GUEST #7:
Something's going up my leg!

SOUND:
The doorbell.

(At the sound of the doorbell, everybody freezes in place.
Harold, Chester, and Howie should end up in funny positions
as everyone stays motionless.)

HAROLD:
(to Chester)
Well, Chester, I think we've blown our image as perfect pets.

(The door opens. Mr. Hu, carrying a sign, enters the living room. Everyone
turns to look at him.)

MR. HU:
Hello, everyone. Thank you for looking after my animals.
Are you ready for the show to begin?

(Everyone "unfreezes" as Mr. Hu crosses to Mrs. Monroe.)

MR. HU:
Mrs. Monroe, how did all my animals get loose?
(Spotting Harold, Chester, and Howie)
And what are *they* doing in here? You know I told you they had to go.

MRS. MONROE:
I'm sorry, Mr. Hu. I have no idea how your animals got loose.
But we'll round them all up, won't we, boys and girls?
(The guests react.)
As for our pets, well . . .

MR. HU:
As for your pets, unless Mr. Kitty-Cat wants to end up
inside Mr. Boa Constrictor, he had better leave the room.
Pronto.

SNAKE:
(to Chester)
What do you say? Shall we do lunch?

CHESTER:
(nervously)
I'm on a diet.

SNAKE:
I'm not.

CHESTER:
(even more nervously)
I'm outta here!

*(**Chester** hightails it out of the living room into the room with the cartons. **Harold** and **Howie** are fast on his heels. They watch the action from the doorway as **Mr. Hu** puts up his sign that reads*
HU'S ZOO: UNUSUAL ANIMALS FOR YOUR PARTY.
*The **Monroes** and the **guests** all gather around, as **Mr. Hu** brings his **animals** into a circle in front of them. He pantomimes, showing the **guests** the **animals** as the others pantomime their reactions.)*

HAROLD:
(reading the sign)
"Hu's Zoo."

HOWIE:
Who's who? Well, I'm Howie. And you're Harold. And —

HAROLD:
*(ignoring **Howie**)*
Nice going, Chester.

CHESTER:
*(as if he has no idea what **Harold** is talking about)*
Why, whatever do you mean, Harold?

HAROLD:
Toby's birthday present, huh? Those animals are the entertainment!

CHESTER:
(explaining patiently)
Harold. Television is entertainment. Books are entertainment.
A ball of yarn is entertainment.
Sitting inside a boa constrictor is not entertainment.

HAROLD:
Right. And that's why we had to go. Mr. Hu didn't want the pets in the same room with the —

CHESTER:
Entertainment. Fine, Harold, you made your point.

HOWIE:
I don't know about anybody else, but all that talk about being eaten has made me hungry.

*(In the living room, the **guests** start to sing "Happy Birthday" to **Toby**.)*

HAROLD:
Let's hope they have a backup cake.

CHESTER:
At least there'll be ice cream.

*(The three **pets** sneak out the door into the living room.)*

CHESTER:
Let's see what's in the kitchen. I'm in the mood for dessert.

*(The **snake** slithers toward **Chester**, **Harold**, and **Howie**.)*

SNAKE:
Did someone say dessert?

*(The **pets** look at each other and make an abrupt U-turn, falling over each other as they rush to the den and go back into hiding. Everyone watches them exit.)*

TOBY:
Mr. Hu?

MR. HU:
Yes?

TOBY:
I like your animals and all. But, trust me, when it comes to unusual, they don't come close to the ones in *this* house!

(Everyone laughs and breaks into another chorus of "Happy Birthday.")

BLACKOUT.